C000162023

LITTLE BOOK OF THE

UNIVERSE

Liam McCann

LITTLE BOOK OF THE

UNIVERSE

First published in the UK in 2012

© Demand Media Limited 2012

www.demand-media.co.uk

Printed and bound in China

ISBN 978-1-909217-16-4

Contents

Introduction

BELOW Nicolaus Copernicus, one of the fathers of modern astronomy, published the landmark book *On the Revolutions of the Celestial Spheres* in 1543.

There are few subjects more fascinating than cosmology – the study of our universe. Although we are yet to explore our deep oceans, and a few small outposts on land remain beyond the reach of our most intrepid adventurers, we have not even scratched the surface when it comes to understanding the seemingly infinite space around us. That space contains all the planets, stars, galaxies, intergalactic space and energy that exist. It also contains a great deal that we know little or nothing about (more on that later).

It was originally believed that the earth was the centre of the universe, and that everything in it revolved around us. As maths and science developed, Copernicus and Newton refined these early ideas and put us in our proper place: the third planet in a solar system where eight planets and countless smaller objects, like asteroids and comets, orbited a yellow sun.

As our telescopes developed, we realised that we were in fact part of a galaxy that contained billions of stars, and that other galaxies existed beyond our own. Indeed, space is so large that we need different concepts to describe it: we've all heard of the light year (the distance that light, travelling at roughly 186,000 miles or 300,000 kilometres per second, travels in one year) but there are also astronomical units and parsecs,

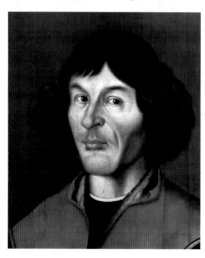

LEFT Sir James Thornhill's portrait of Sir Isaac Newton.

amongst others. An astronomical unit is the distance from the earth to the sun, which is around 93 million miles (150 million kilometres). And a parsec is the distance from the sun to any object that has a parallax angle of one arcsecond, which turns out to be 3.26 light years. If this sounds complicated, it's just based on the movement of cosmic objects relative to one another. Imaginary right-angled triangles can be traced between them and the trigonometry learned at school can then be used to calculate the distance that separates them.

When it comes to exploring something the size of our universe, light will have to be our medium. It is just possible to see the M31 Galaxy in the constellation Andromeda with the naked eye. Although our telescopes reveal this to be a massive spiral galaxy, it's 2.5 million light years or 15 billion billion miles (around 25 billion billion kilometres) away so it only appears as a faint smudge in the sky near the W of Cassiopeia. Of course, the furthest someone has travelled from the earth is the 240,000 miles (385,000 kilometres) to the moon so we clearly have much to learn from the wider cosmos.

Humans are a curious species; we have always wondered where we came from, and where we are going. We'd like to know how the universe started, if there was anything before it, how and when it will end, if there is other life out there, and a million other questions that one day we hope to answer. We've discovered more about ourselves and our surroundings in the last century than in all of human history to that point, so we live in exciting times. Who knows what we'll discover next.

FAR LEFT The Andromeda Galaxy (M31) seen through a hydrogen-alpha filter.

ABOVE Together with Bob Wilson, Arno Penzias helped discover the cosmic microwave background radiation left over after the Big Bang.

The Big Bang

Ever since we were at school we have been told by physicists that there was nothing before the Big Bang and then, all of a sudden, from this nothingness our universe – and all the energy and matter it would eventually need – exploded into life. This description troubles

us because it seems a) difficult to comprehend and b) impossible. How do we get something from nothing? And what happened beforehand?

Physicists like to explain both concepts by baffling you with the science, but the reality is, for all their wonderful equations that help explain why the universe is the way it is today, they don't have answers to either of these questions, only theories. Some now believe that the rapid expansion after the Big Bang is part of a cycle, others that these explosions occur all the time when two parallel universes collide, and still more that this is what happens inside the singularity at the centre of a super-massive black hole. Of course there is another solution: all of it was brought into existence by a creator. Although most scientists will dismiss this notion immediately, the questions do have a religious significance because many of us believe a divine being lit the fuse.

Until we have an answer, which

LEFT The WMAP image of the cosmic microwave background. The different colours represent tiny fluctuations in the temperature of the universe.

may never happen, most cosmologists are happy to stand by the standard model. The initial explosion was so hot that it first created an almost infinite amount of raging energy. After only around a second, some of this energy was transformed into the seeds of matter (Einstein's famous $E=mc^2$ equation – of which more later – tells us that mass and energy have an equivalence so matter can be created from pure energy). You may ask where all this happened, but the answer is equally perplexing because it happened everywhere. All of space came into existence from one point, so it started from wherever you can imagine: in front of your face, in the centre of the earth, or in the farthest reaches of the cosmos.

Finding the remnants of this initial explosion was what forced scientists to conclude that it must have happened. Beforehand, there had been two competing theories. The steady-state theory suggested that the universe had always existed in its current form and it

THE BIG BANG

would continue largely unchanged until the end of time. It was supported by such notable names as Fred Hoyle (who coined the phrase *Big Bang* derisively to show his disgust for the theory) and Thomas Gold. The Big Bang, by contrast, was not widely accepted until 1965 when two young radio astronomers, Arno Penzias and Bob Wilson, discovered constant background interference in the data they were collecting on radio waves from communication satellites. No matter how hard they tried to eliminate it (this included cleaning pigeon droppings from the antenna), it persisted from every corner of the sky, day and night.

Forty miles away at Princeton University, a team under Robert Dicke was searching for microwave radiation left over after the Big Bang. Penzias and Wilson heard about their search and concluded they'd found what Dicke was looking for: the cosmic microwave background. The length of time and enormous distance travelled by the heat and light meant that the after-effects of the explosion had been converted into microwaves, a theory suggested by astrophysicist George Gamow. This radiation can be seen when you detune your television as about one percent of the static is the microwave background.

The next phase was one of expansion. This was no ordinary expansion because the entire universe was inside the space that was expanding, and it still is. Within an instant, the universe is believed to have expanded to around 100 billion light years across. This seems to break the cosmic light-speed limit but it was space itself that was expanding (another difficult concept to grasp).

We're lucky that the physical forces in our universe all seem to be at the right comparative strength. Let's take gravity: if it had been stronger, the universe might not have expanded at all and would have collapsed back on itself instead; if it had been weaker, maybe no galaxies or stars or you and I would ever have formed. The conversion rate of hydrogen to helium inside stars is also finely balanced in our favour. A little tweak and none of the remaining elements could form. It's possible, of course, that there were countless previous attempts at building a universe before our one finally worked.

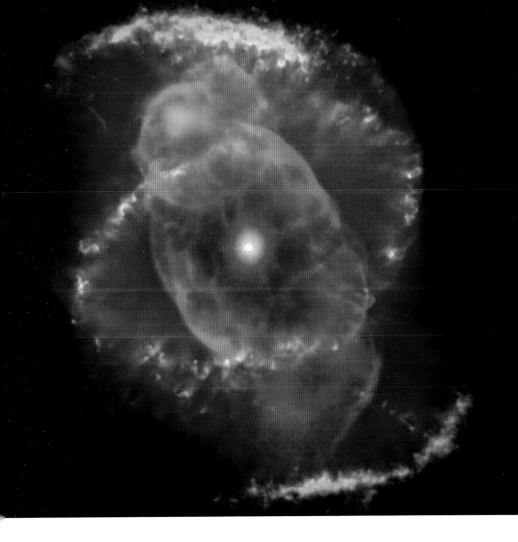

It would take another 380,000 years before the subatomic particles began to form that would eventually coalesce into all of the stars, galaxies and planets that make up our universe today. After about a billion years, enough of this matter had accumulated in one place and reached such a size and density that the pressure inside it became so great that it forced the hydrogen atoms to fuse, heating up to 10 million degrees before sparking into life and light. Matter formed just after the Big Bang had been converted back into pure energy: the first star had been born. As gravity continued its work, more stars formed, until they too attracted one another and gave birth to the first galaxy.

There are problems with the standard model, however. The more we study the night sky, the more we realise things aren't exactly as they should be. If we take the Big Bang as a conventional explosion, the universe would be uneven and random. Explosions are extremely difficult to predict and inherently untidy. There would be hot and cold patches, as well as light and dark areas distributed all over the night sky. But the universe is not like this at all. Its temperature is almost uniform in every direction.

Professor Alan Guth tried to tackle these problems by incorporating a theory of inflation because no normal explosion would result in the uniformity of our universe. Inflation theory said the universe may have remained small while the heat within it (the cosmic microwave background) dispersed evenly, and then the rapid inflation took over.

By mapping the cosmic microwave background, aside from tiny fluctuations of as little as $1/10,000$th of a degree, the temperature was the same in all directions. There are problems with inflation because nothing like it has ever been witnessed, whether in the real world or in the lab. And the inflation theory also only allows for matter and energy to be present in the universe. As we shall see in a later chapter, dark matter shouldn't have a place in the standard model because it neither emits nor absorbs light, so it remains tantalisingly out of reach.

There are more problems with the rate of the universe's expansion. All the observable matter in the universe (as well as the dark matter) should be exerting a gravitational force on all the other matter, and this should be slowing the universe's expansion. But the universe is actually getting bigger at an increasing rate as if the Big Bang

THE BIG BANG

explosion is ongoing. (It's a matter of contention among physicists as to whether it is just the space between galaxies that is expanding, or all of space. If it were just intergalactic space, how would the boundary between expanding space and the space within a galaxy be defined? If it were all of space, you'd think we'd be able to measure it happening in our own solar system, or even within ourselves.) If the explosion really is ongoing something would have to be powering this expansion. This will also be explored in a later chapter.

Despite initial doubts as to how dark matter and the other unexplained phenomena could fit into the standard model, the fact that the Big Bang and then inflation theories hold up to close scrutiny only makes them stronger. Until the Big Bang is disproved, possibly by string theory (which will finally explain quantum gravity and give physicists their Holy Grail: a theory of everything), it will remain the basis for the maths and physics of the universe around us.

So, as more stars came into existence, their gravitational fields drew them together until they formed enormous galaxies. As these stars went through their life cycles, they burned hydrogen and combined some of it to form helium, which is what gives the star its energy. Helium is slightly heavier than hydrogen so it sinks to the centre of the star. As helium atoms fuse together under the enormous pressures in a star's centre, more energy is released and more elements – in a process known as nucleosynthesis – are formed: gold, silver, iron, carbon and oxygen. When these stars near the end of their lives, the internal pressure falls as the helium runs out and they collapse. The resulting pressure forms all of the remaining elements found in our universe, which are then blasted off into space during the supernova explosion. These elements will eventually coalesce under gravity to form the planets.

It's strange to think that every atom that makes up you and me started off in the centre of a collapsing star but this is the standard model of cosmology and the accepted picture of how we got where we are today. So let's move closer to home and take a look at our galaxy.

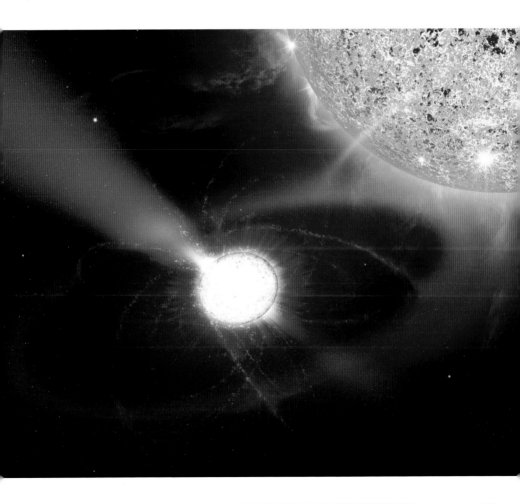

The Milky Way

one of the oldest spiral galaxies in the cosmos and may have begun to coalesce around 12 billion years ago. In brightly lit areas, such as in a city centre, you will never be able to see it, but move into the country on a dark, cloudless, moonless night and it will be revealed. The stars near its centre form a bar that was confirmed by the Spitzer Space Telescope in 2005.

The Milky Way is around 120,000 light years across, 1,000 light years thick and contains about 200 billion stars and their accompanying systems. (Aside from the odd smudge of distant galaxies, every star we can see with the naked eye is in our galaxy. You may be surprised to find that only around 3,000 stars can be seen from any one position on earth, considerably fewer if you live in a city with its light pollution.) The number of stars in the Milky Way is too large for the scale to be appreciated, but if we can imagine a grain of sand between the centre circle and the penalty area on a football

Our galaxy was so named because it appears as a milky band that arches across the night sky. Because we are looking at it from the inside, it seems like a flattish disc. Although we can't be certain, we think it's

pitch, that would correspond roughly with our entire solar system and where it fits within the galaxy. Our nearest star (other than the sun), Proxima Centauri, and its accompanying system, would be another grain of sand 1/6th of an inch (four millimetres) away.

We have only found a few planets outside our solar system because they are difficult to locate at such great distances, but we know there are eight planets and countless smaller asteroids and comets orbiting our own sun, so it's fair to say there must be billions of them in our galaxy. Of these, many

hundreds of millions will be in the habitable zone where sunlight warms the surface so that liquid water can exist.

Our solar system is on the inner edge of the Orion-Cygnus Arm 30,000 light years from the galactic centre. As the band of stars divides our night sky into two roughly equal hemispheres, we know that our sun must lie close to the galactic plane.

As we approach the centre, the Milky Way bulges so it is really shaped like two fried eggs placed back to back. This enormous mass of stars, dust and gas is moving through the cosmos at around 370 miles (600 kilometres) per second. Speed on this scale is difficult to measure because you need a point to compare it with for it to make any sense. The same is true for time. It's all very well saying that the Milky Way is 12 billion years old but time ticks at different rates depending on gravity and speed so we have defined its age relative to the number of years that have passed on Earth. The entire galaxy also rotates about once every 25 million years.

The Milky Way is surrounded by a galactic halo of stars and globular clusters (a group of stars that has clumped together and acts like a satellite orbiting the galaxy) that rarely approach within 180,000 light years.

Our neighbouring galaxy, Andromeda, is much larger and probably contains a trillion stars, five times that of the Milky Way. It's also a very long way away. On the same scale as our football pitch, it would be 1.5 miles (2.5 kilometres) distant.

It was always believed that the billions of solar systems that made up a galaxy orbited a series of larger stars at the galactic centre. We now know of course that at the centre of most

galaxies a much more powerful and largely misunderstood beast lurks in the shadows: a black hole. The one in the Milky Way was discovered because it emits an intense radio source known as Sagittarius A★ (pronounced A-star).

There are several theories about how and why black holes form. Some people believe that they are massive stars that have such a powerful gravitational pull that not even light can escape. This is relatively easy to test. On Earth, if you fire a bullet into the sky, it will soon yield to gravity (and air resistance) and fall back to the ground. We know that an object needs to be fired at around seven miles (11 kilometres) per second if it is to overcome the earth's gravity, reach escape velocity and make it into orbit.

If our planet were much larger or denser (or both) it would distort space-time even more and any object fired into orbit would need to be travelling much faster to reach escape velocity. Clearly this can be extrapolated further. Could there be an object so massive (not necessarily large – it could also be small but extremely dense) that distorted space-time so much

that its escape velocity exceeded the speed of light? The answer is yes.

Because light can't escape, however, we can't be sure if the invisible mass is actually an enormous star-like object or an incredibly dense but much smaller entity that could be no bigger than a marble. Conventional wisdom suggests

that black holes are formed when stars run out of hydrogen fuel and collapse in on themselves under their enormous gravity (because there's no longer any nuclear fusion going on inside the star, its interior pressure falls and it can no longer resist its own gravity). When the star collapses it usually explodes in a supernova, blowing all its remaining gas and dust out into space. At its centre, however, heavier atoms remain. They are crushed by enormous gravitational forces until a black hole forms and actually tears a hole in the fabric of space-time. This, however, appears to contravene the accepted laws of physics so we still have much to learn about black holes.

In an ideal universe, a supernova explosion would happen in the Milky

Way and we could study it. But there are two problems with this: they don't happen very often (one was visible during the day in China in 1054, which created the Crab Nebula, another couple were seen in the Middle Ages, and one flared in the Large Magellanic Cloud 170,000 light years away in 1987); and, secondly, if one went off too close to us, it would destroy our planet. The solution is to use a supercomputer to model the collapse of a star to try to predict what happens after the explosion. The models throw up some interesting results, however. It appears that some black holes might form quietly without the explosion. The star simply collapses under its own gravity and disappears in a process known as going un-nova.

We now believe that a small but extremely dense object is the basis for a black hole. If the sun were shrunk down to only a few kilometres across, for example, it would be so dense and its gravitational field so strong that not even light would be able to escape. As light is the fastest thing we know of, if it can't be emitted into space, nothing should be visible:

this is a black hole. But this doesn't adequately explain what's going on at the centre of our galaxy.

In 1931 Karl Jansky was experimenting with radio waves in the hope that it would lead to a trans-Atlantic telephone service. But his experiments were plagued by background interference. He eventually concluded that most of the static was caused by thunderstorms. The propagation of the remaining interference seemed to coincide with the rotation of the earth, however, so he concluded that it must be caused by the sun. When he refined his experiments, he discovered that the signal actually repeated every 23 hours and 56 minutes and was linked with the earth's position not in the solar system but in the galaxy. He then traced the source of the static to the constellation Sagittarius, which was close to the galactic centre.

Everyone agreed that the signal couldn't be produced by a star so they began to wonder if it might be coming from the then-theoretical black hole. The problem was that the centre of the galaxy was obscured by a veil of dust and gas and it remained just

LEFT
Stephen Hawking with daughter Lucy at NASA's 50th anniversary party in 2008.

out of sight. Infrared light, however, could penetrate this dust. In 1992, it was discovered that a dense collection of stars was orbiting something at the centre of the Milky Way.

Over the next 20 years, teams at the Max Planck Institute plotted the positions of these stars relative to one another and the galactic centre. They discovered that unlike in the outer arms of the galaxy, where stars were moving at similar speeds, the stars closest to the centre were orbiting a common, dark and extremely dense point at tremendous velocity (one was clocked at 11 million miles per hour / 17 million kilometres /h). And it was from here that the radio signal emanated.

Using the standard candle method for measuring star size (and therefore mass and density), it was calculated that the object they were orbiting had a mass approximately four million times that of our sun. It could only mean one thing: at the centre of our galaxy there was a super-massive black hole. And to reach its current mass, it must have devoured millions of stars during its lifetime.

The more galaxies the team at the institute studied, the more black holes they found. It turns out that nearly every galaxy has one at its centre, some more than a billion times more massive than our sun. From others, they found unusual patterns in the rotation of the stars, and radio signals they weren't expecting. The conclusion was that when ancient galaxies collided, their black holes didn't join forces but ended up rotating about one another. (The pattern of rotation, incidentally, closely mimics the way electrons fuzz around the nucleus of an atom, so there may be more connections between the world of the very large and the quantum world than we originally thought.)

This potential connection has led to a clash of theories proposed by two of the greatest living physicists. Stephen Hawking has devoted his life to combining the physics of the very large and the very small (quantum mechanics), but, although a grand unifying theory could be just over the horizon, it remains out of reach for now.

Quantum mechanics predicts that the cosmos should be bubbling with virtual particles popping into and out of existence as matter and antimatter are produced spontaneously from pure energy (made possible by the $E=mc^2$ equation) before annihilating one another and releasing the original energy. (This is why scientists want to harness antimatter because when it annihilates with matter it releases pure energy that could power our cities or spacecraft of the future.)

These particles usually annihilate one another, but there is one place in the universe where they can enter reality. Surrounding a black hole is its event horizon, which is the barrier between where light can escape and where it cannot. If these pairs of virtual particles spontaneously came into existence at the event horizon, one particle would escape and one would be drawn into the black hole before they could annihilate each another. The particle that escapes should be visible as what has become known as Hawking Radiation, a faint light that should guide us to these black holes. But because no one has detected this radiation yet (it would be extremely faint and black holes are a long way away), it leaves the eminent physicist's work open to attack from rival cosmologists.

One of the fathers of string theory, and a leading theoretical physicist, Leonard Susskind disagrees with the Hawking version of the universe. Hawking claimed that black holes like the one at the centre of the Milky Way violated the laws of conservation of information because anything that ended up in one was lost from our universe forever. Susskind countered that the information may not be visible and would be difficult to retrieve, but it did still exist, and it did not therefore violate the established physical laws.

Susskind backed up his argument by saying that although a nuclear explosion may appear to destroy everything in its vicinity, the fallout, detritus and information about the explosion are still contained within our universe. Hawking's version had black holes devouring information, removing it from the universe and destroying it forever. The battle lines had been drawn, but Susskind needed proof if he was going to challenge the Hawking view.

He turned his attention to the event horizon. If two people approach the boundary and one of them (let's call her Jill) crosses it, how would they both experience what happened next? The person looking at Jill (let's call him Jack) would see her move towards the event horizon. As the enormous gravitational pull of a black hole distorts both space and time, Jack would see her slow down until she (and time) stopped.

Jill, on the other hand, would pass through the event horizon and then be torn to pieces by the immense gravity of the black hole. Depending on your point of view, the outcome of the situation would be completely different, and the two outcomes were clearly at odds with one another. From Jack's point of view Jill is stationary but technically alive. You wouldn't want to be in Jill's position, however.

Susskind concluded that as Jill appeared to slow down (from Jack's perspective) more information about her could be determined. He used the analogy of an aircraft's propeller. If it is spinning at full speed, you can only see the central hub, but slow it down and the blades gradually come into focus. The distortion of time itself is the key. Inside the black hole, Jill may appear to be lost forever, but the information about her is stored at the event horizon, not in the three dimensions that we are used to but in two dimensions as a kind of hologram. Everything that falls into the black hole does therefore leave its signature in the visible universe and information is not lost. In 2004, Hawking conceded defeat at a conference in Dublin.

His admission opened up the startling possibility that although we are all three-dimensional beings, we could also exist as scrambled bundles of two-dimensional information out there in the cosmos. That black holes, like the one at the centre of the Milky Way, could store this information at their event horizons may be hard to believe, but some physicists think they could also be used for travelling through time.

Time Travel

RIGHT
Theoretical
physicist Michio
Kaku believes
time travel may
one day become
reality.

The notion of travelling through time may still seem like it belongs in the pages of a science-fiction novel, but plenty of respectable physicists now believe it's possible to manipulate both space and time. It's time to find out whether the theories can become reality.

For theoretical physicists Ron Mallett and Michio Kaku, time itself must be understood before we have any chance of travelling through it. When we look at our reflection in the mirror, light has to travel from our face to the mirror and then back to our eye. Although this takes time, light travels so fast we don't notice it at such small distances. When we look at the sun, however, we're seeing it as it was around eight minutes ago because that's how long its light has taken to cross the 93 million miles (150 million kilometres) of intervening space to reach Earth. If it suddenly exploded (don't worry, this shouldn't happen for another five billion years), we wouldn't initially notice any difference (and we'd hardly register it when the light reached us anyway because we'd be dead a moment later). When we look at an object that's much further away, through a telescope at our neighbouring Andromeda Galaxy for example, we see it not as it is now but as it was 2.5 million years ago.

Some properties of time must also be understood. Many people think that if it's midday where they are, it should be midday throughout the universe because time runs at a constant speed. Unfortunately, this isn't true. Einstein's Theory of General Relativity tells us that the speed at which time ticks, somewhat confusingly, depends on how fast you're moving and how strong gravity is. The faster you travel, the slower your clock ticks so you age more slowly; under a strong gravitational field it also ticks slower (this has real-world implications for anyone using GPS).

On the surface of the earth, the effect of gravity is reasonably constant.

The further you travel from the centre of its mass, however, the faster a clock will tick. GPS satellites orbit around 12,600 miles (20,200 kilometres) from our planet, so their clocks tick a little faster. But the satellites are moving through space at 8,700 mph (14,700 km/h), which means their clocks would tick a little slower. The net result is that the atomic clocks on the satellites tick faster than those on Earth. They are so sensitive, however, that even a difference of a tiny fraction of a second between the clocks on the ground and those in space can have dramatic consequences for those using the system. If the clocks weren't adjusted several times a day to allow for these differences, your GPS could send you off course by up to seven miles (11 kilometres).

Astronauts travelling to the international space station have spent many months hurtling through space much faster than the rest of us, and, because of their low orbit and extremely high speed (18,000 mph / 27,000 km/h), they have time-travelled a few milliseconds into the future. On this scale, it's difficult to imagine how time-travel to the distant past or future might become a possibility, but if we increase the speed things get more interesting.

Spaceships of the future will be simply enormous. They will accelerate for a few years and burn up enormous amounts of fuel (possibly provided by the sun or other stars). As they approach the speed of light, they will begin to travel through time. A journey to the edge of the Milky Way that would have taken millions of years in a conventional spacecraft would only take 80 years in this one. There are obvious problems with this – the cost of building the ship and supplying it with fuel being just two – so scientists are again looking at ways to travel through time on Earth.

Imagine one twin brother gets on a train that can travel extremely fast. The train accelerates until it is travelling at just below the speed of light (as this would mean circumnavigating the earth seven times every second, it's not going to happen soon), at which point time onboard begins to slow down. The passengers wouldn't notice this as their time remains unchanged – it is only relative to everyone else on Earth.

The brother on the train then

LEFT An artist's impression of a Navstar GPS satellite.

gets out of his seat and runs along the aisle. If his speed is added to the train's forward motion it would seem that he'd broken the light barrier. As this appears to contravene the laws of physics, which, despite a scare with some neutrinos at CERN recently, is still impossible, something else must be responsible for the anomaly. The answer is known as time dilation. The clock on the train must actually be running slower to protect the cosmic speed limit because the speed of light remains constant for both twins. The effect is so pronounced that if passengers stayed on the train for a week, a hundred years would have passed for the rest of us. This is time-travelling on a scale that has scientists excited.

It's clearly not possible for us to test this thought experiment with our current technology, however, because we have no propulsion system that can accelerate a person to anywhere near the speed of light, let alone an entire train or spaceship. But we can accelerate particles, in the Large Hadron Collider at CERN – the European centre for nuclear research – in Switzerland, for example, to within a sniff of terminal velocity. Muons or Pi mesons tend to be the particles of choice because they usually only exist for millionths of a second and are difficult to study. When they are accelerated towards the speed of light, they exist for up to 30 times longer because their clocks have slowed down relative to ours.

There is another problem with accelerating objects towards the speed of light. As the speed increases, so does the object's mass. With a tiny almost massless particle like a muon, this isn't a major problem, although it still weighs 7,000 times more than it would at rest. If you want to build a spacecraft or train to travel at near light-speed, it becomes the main hurdle. As the object accelerates it becomes heavier and heavier. This means it needs more energy to propel it faster. As you approach the speed of light, you need an infinite amount of energy to keep the object accelerating, which we cannot supply with current technologies.

Despite these obstacles, it is theoretically possible to move through time into the future, even if it's not by very much. So, what would our time-travellers have to do if they wanted

to come back and tell us their story?

There are other ways despite speed to manipulate space-time. Gravity can also help us move through it. Everything in the universe with mass distorts space-time by some degree, and that includes all of us, the mountains, continents, planets, stars, galaxies and black holes, with the larger structures warping the fabric more than the smaller objects. This phenomenon can be observed by studying HST photographs of the light from distant galaxies. The galaxy itself bends the light like a lens and creates a halo, which is overwhelming evidence that the mass of the galaxy is distorting space-time and therefore the passage of light itself.

It is perhaps easiest to imagine space-time as a thin but pliable sheet spread over a large hole. An iron ball dropped onto the sheet will cause it to sag, which is a little like how the sun warps space-time. If you roll a marble (the earth) across the sheet, it will arc towards the larger, heavier ball as if snared by gravity until it ends up in orbit. Of course, the marble will eventually crash into the iron ball because it is static. Roll the larger ball across the sheet and the marble will follow it. If there was no resistance from the sheet and we were conducting this experiment in the three-dimensional vacuum of space, their motion would mimic the earth and the sun in the solar system. This model can be shrunk to fit the earth and the moon, or enlarged to explain how the sun orbits the galactic centre (it only seems to break down at the quantum level inside atoms and when the larger universe is examined). Indeed, some have posited that gravity itself doesn't really exist – the motion of the planets and stars is merely a product of the warping of space-time.

This is the basis for Einstein's Theory of General Relativity, which was quite a piece of work for a young German-born patent clerk with no background in physics. Unlike Special Relativity (which gave us his equation $E=mc^2$ and merely explained how stars could burn for so long by releasing energy from the hydrogen-helium nucleosynthesis, and how radiation could be emitted from a lump of uranium without it melting like an ice cube), which might have been proposed by the likes of Max Planck or J Willard Gibbs in the

early 19th century, we would probably still be waiting for someone to come up with General Relativity, even though its effects can be measured in our everyday lives. Indeed, the latter has been called the greatest single idea in the history of physics, and, considering the man himself rarely supplied all his working, it was almost as if he just thought about the problems of the universe and then came up with the answers out of thin air.

As we have seen before with the GPS satellites, when large objects like Earth distort space-time, the passage of time is also affected. But the effect on Earth is not enough to help the would-be time-traveller. The object would need to be much larger, like a black hole. Scientists now believe that many super-massive black holes are spinning at close to the speed of light, dragging space-time with them, which then forms almost a complete circle. If the time-traveller were to cross the diameter, they could theoretically outrun a beam of light that would have to make the longer journey around the circumference. This would enable them to arrive back before they had left, and

LEFT Albert Einstein shortly after receiving his Nobel Prize for Physics in 1921.

TIME TRAVEL

they would have travelled back in time.

There are problems with this too, however, as it would almost certainly involve crossing the event horizon, which is a one-way trip to oblivion. The second problem is equally large: to manipulate the fabric of space-time and travel a single year into the past would require a mass half the size of the entire galaxy. And the third major obstacle would be what Steven Hawking calls a feedback loop.

The eminent physicist has often wondered why no one has appeared from the future. If time-travel ever became possible, surely someone would have come back to let us know. He imagines hosting a party for travellers from the future. You can do it yourself. The trouble is, no one will turn up, and this is usually attributed to the paradoxes that exist when discussing travel to the past. The most common of these is known as the grandfather paradox, and it involves going back in time to kill your ancestor before your father has been conceived. If your father hasn't even been conceived, how can you exist?

Hawking foresees more problems with a variation known as the mad scientist paradox. If the scientist has managed to create a wormhole in his lab that stretches just one minute into the past, he can engineer his own paradox. He passes through the wormhole and looks back to see himself a minute earlier. If he shoots himself through the wormhole, he should be dead before he even entered the time machine. This begs the question as to who fired the shot.

Time machines of this nature breaks one of the fundamental laws of the universe: causes happen before effects, and never the other way round. These laws must be obeyed or the entire universe would be a chaotic and extremely dangerous place. Hawking believes that something must happen to prevent the scientist from getting into a position where he can shoot himself. The wormhole itself appears to be the problem, and this is where feedback slides into the equation.

When sound enters a microphone at a concert, it is transmitted to the amplifier and projected through the speakers. If it is too loud, the microphone will pick it up and

re-amplify it, causing the sound to feedback in a high-pitched screech that can damage the amplifier and speakers. Hawking believes the same phenomenon will be observed in a wormhole. Radiation will be sucked into the time tunnel and magnified until the wormhole collapses. As this will happen almost instantaneously,

a wormhole is unlikely to be around long enough for us to use one.

Using a short cut between two points in space is still the best option available to the time-traveller, however. This is where a wormhole at the centre of a black hole comes into play; we know black holes exist and they appear to stick around for some time. If they link

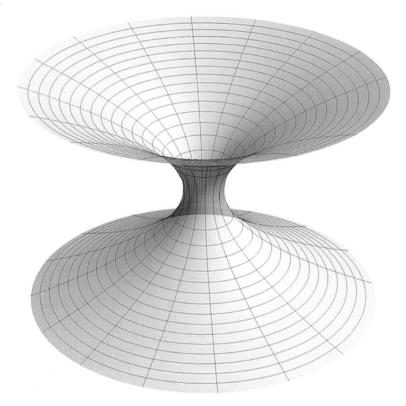

two points in space that we could cross faster than light takes around the longer, curved route, and providing we could survive the extreme gravity, we might one day be able to harness this power.

In the quantum world, there are

already crinkles and holes in the fabric of space-time but they are too small to be seen or used. However, Hawking believes they do link separate places and different times. His theory is backed up by our observations on the behaviour of electrons that appear to be in more than one place at the same time. They use tiny wormholes inside atoms to make the famous quantum leap.

So why did no one come back from the future to Hawking's party? Either wormholes can't be used, or the machine that allows us to create wormholes hasn't yet been invented. Wouldn't it be strange if as soon as such a machine was finished, someone from the future appeared inside it? Only then would we know if the machine we'd built works because, like telephones, we'd need a receiver to be able to connect our call with the future.

Ron Mallett believes we may be able to manufacture useable wormholes much sooner than we thought, however. He wants to use rotating beams of light to replicate the frame-dragging properties found in super-massive black holes. If his lasers can distort space-time, they could create a tiny time loop.

Although sending something as massive as a person or spaceship back in time may be beyond Mallett's machine (and it could have dire consequences for the present if the time-traveller altered the course of history, whether deliberately or inadvertently), he believes it may be possible to send information back from the future. What if we could send ourselves cures for diseases or warnings of future catastrophes?

If the black hole can't help us travel back in time, maybe it can assist us in moving forward to the future. The one at the centre of our galaxy is so massive that time slows right down in its immense gravitational field. Hawking believes that if we had a spaceship that could circle it just outside the event horizon (at the right speed to prevent it being sucked in), it would be pulled into orbit. At this incredible speed, each orbit for the people in the spaceship would take a different amount of time than for those monitoring the mission. Speed itself plays a part in moving through time, and so does the massive gravity of the black hole. In fact, time would only tick half as quickly for those on the spaceship. If they circled the black hole for five years, 10 years would have passed on Earth: they would have travelled another five years into the future.

LEFT
A Lorentzian wormhole (Schwarzschild wormhole).

TIME TRAVEL

BELOW Artist concept of Gravity Probe B orbiting the Earth to measure space-time, a four-dimensional description of the universe including height, width, length, and time.

Seeing time as a mechanical constant is therefore pointless – it must be viewed as a dimension that is part of the fabric of space. This means that we actually live in a world of four dimensions, three of which (up/down, left/right and forward/backward) are familiar to us. But these three dimensions on their own are not enough to get by in the real world. You can arrange to meet someone anywhere on Earth by giving them accurate grid coordinates, but unless you supply the correct time for the meeting, you will not make your rendezvous. (Some believe that the familiar three dimensions are a little arbitrary: we may be able to move

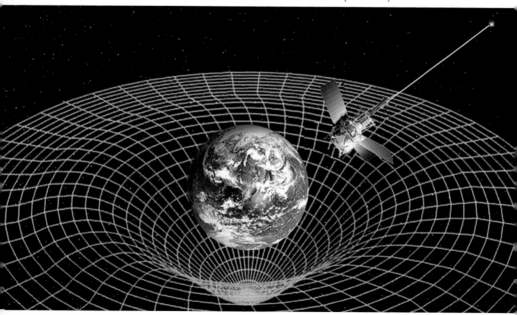

up and down, left and right, and forwards and backwards but these are really only directions in space. We're not actually moving in several dimensions when we walk diagonally uphill, just the one: space-time.)

Physicists now believe that space-time can be bent and stretched, and maybe even folded back on itself, which is what a time machine would have to do. As we are still unable to manage this, perhaps we should concentrate on a place and time that is more familiar to us.

ABOVE Artist impression of a binary system with an accretion disk around a black hole being fed by material from the companion star.

Our Solar System

Our sun lies on one of the outer arms of the Milky Way Galaxy about 30,000 light years from the black hole at its centre. (It's always been assumed that the Milky Way looks like a spiral but, as we're inside it, we can't actually see it.) The sun was formed by the accumulation of hydrogen atoms under gravity. When enough matter had collected, the heat and pressure built up and it burst into life.

Even though our parent star is considered to be a yellow dwarf, it is truly enormous. At around 900,000 miles (1.4 million kilometres) across, it is more than 100 times the diameter of the earth, 1.3 million times its volume and 330,000 times as massive. Its plasma is also extremely hot with temperatures at its surface around 5,500°C (9,932°F) and 16 million Celsius (28 million Fahrenheit) at its core. (Its light is actually almost pure white but it appears yellow because our atmosphere scatters some wavelengths.)

The main elements found on Earth were formed when an ancient star ran out of fuel, collapsed under its own mass and exploded. All of the iron,

Mercury Venus Earth Mars Jupiter Saturn Uranus Neptune

PLANETS

DWARF PLANETS

Ceres

Pluto Haumea Makemake Eris

silicon, oxygen and nitrogen created by nucleosynthesis were ejected into space where it eventually began to coalesce. (Similar elementary clouds of matter can still be seen in the universe today – they are the magnificent nebulae.) The earth was born from stardust and assembled by gravity until, after about a hundred million years, it reached its present size. The remaining seven planets, at least 170 moons and countless dwarf planets

all formed under similar circumstances. (Although there is probably enough debris in the asteroid belt to form another planet, Jupiter's gravity seems to be preventing it from coalescing.)

Although the planets have now coalesced and seem relatively peaceful, the solar system is still a dangerous place. Asteroids and comets constantly cross their orbits and occasionally collide with them. There is evidence of these

ABOVE
Illustrating the size difference between the planets and our Sun.

LEFT The sun pictured by NASA's solar dynamics observatory.

RIGHT
Meteor Crater
was originally
thought to have
been caused by
an underground
steam explosion
rather than an
impact from
space.

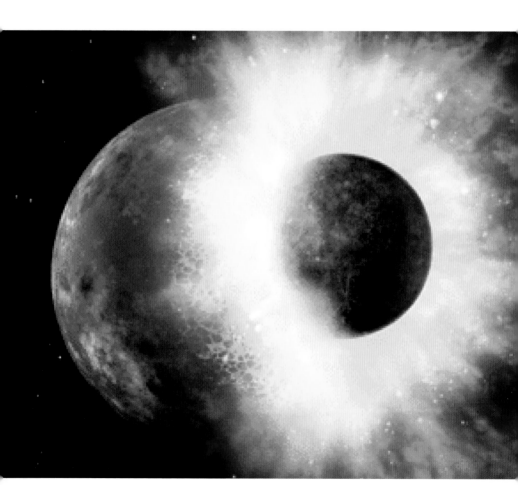

impacts everywhere, such as the craters on the moon. Because the moon has no atmosphere, plate tectonics or other erosive forces, the scars on its surface are plain for us to see. The obvious question is, why do we not see the same impacts on Earth? The answer is simple: erosion. Earth has been battered by asteroids and comets for its entire life (mainly during the late heavy bombardment around half a billion to a billion years after its initial formation), but wind, water and the movement of its crust have eroded the obvious signs. Occasionally an impact crater can be seen. This is because it either happened recently or it's in a place where erosion happens very slowly. A good example is the Barringer (Meteor) Crater in Arizona, which, although it is a mile across, was probably caused by a rock only 300 feet (90 metres) wide.

Mercury

Mercury is the closest planet to the sun and frequently approaches to within 29 million miles (46 million kilometres) of our star. It is a small, rocky planet that is peppered with impact craters, much like our moon. It must be rich

in metals and silicates to account for its high density. It orbits the sun once every 88 days and rotates around its own axis once every 56 days. These two facts give Mercury an extremely interesting calendar. Being only a shade larger than our moon, the planet does not have a large enough gravitational pull to cling onto any gases and form an atmosphere. It is therefore a hot and desolate place where it is extremely doubtful that any life could exist.

ABOVE Looking a little like our moon, Mercury is rich in metals and silicates but is much hotter.

LEFT An artist's impression of the cataclysmic collision between a Mars-size object and the young Earth that gave birth to the moon.

Venus

If Mercury is rather like our moon in composition and size, Venus is much more like Earth. The planet is the brightest natural object in the night sky after the moon and is classified as a terrestrial planet. It may be our twin in size but it certainly isn't in weather. Venus has clouds of sulphuric acid locking in the extreme heat of the sun, and its carbon dioxide-rich atmosphere exerts 92 times the

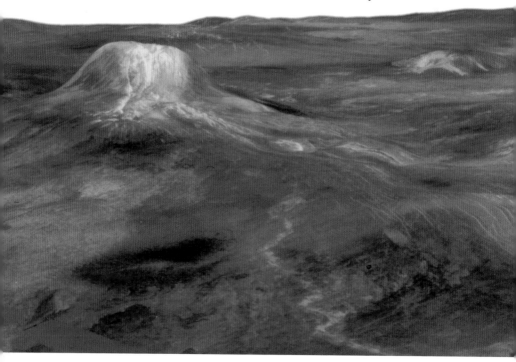

pressure at its surface. This is the equivalent of a water column 3,300 feet (1 kilometre) deep. It may once have been habitable but a runaway greenhouse effect and fierce volcanism has rendered its surface ferociously hot and completely inhospitable. Because it orbits the sun every 225 days and rotates on its axis once every 243 days, its day is actually longer than its year.

Earth

Sometime early in the earth's history, probably as it was cooling after reaching its present size, it was struck by an enormous object about the size of Mars. Part of the object was incorporated into the earth and part was blown off into space where it eventually coalesced and formed the moon. This slow-speed impact knocked the earth into a different orbit, started it spinning in the opposite direction and increased the mass of the earth's iron core. All these factors contributed to the surface conditions that were essential for life to evolve.

The earth is the largest of the four terrestrial planets. Of these, it has the highest density, strongest magnetic field and the greatest surface gravity. Condensing water vapour and more liquids transported through space in comets delivered enough water to the earth for the oceans to form. Being a dense, rocky object, Earth's gravity prevented water vapour and other gases escaping into space after these collisions, so conditions were right for an atmosphere to form. Around a billion years later, life appeared in the oceans and began releasing oxygen from the water which gradually thickened the planet's atmosphere.

The earth is roughly 93 million miles (150 million kilometres) from the sun so it orbits once every 365.26 days. It is tilted at an angle of 23.4° (another handy consequence of the impact in its early life), which gives us our seasons. The gravitational pull from the moon

BELOW An Apollo capsual looking down upon the Earth

also gives us our tides and stabilises the earth, a vital ingredient in allowing life to form and flourish (the earth and moon are really a twin planetary system because it is far larger when compared with its parent planet than all the remaining moons in the solar system).

The Moon

Our moon is around a quarter of the diameter of the earth, and it is the fifth largest satellite in the solar system. Its orbital period around the earth is the same as its rotational period about its own axis so it only shows us one of its hemispheres. Its composition is like that of the earth's crust (giving credence to Reginald Daly's initial theory – which was then backed up by William Hartmann and Donald Davis – that it was formed when much of the earth's crust was blasted into orbit after a cosmic collision).

This collision would have been pretty spectacular: an object the size of Mars struck the juvenile Earth at an oblique angle but the enormous amount of ejecta was soon captured by the earth's gravity. Most scientists believe that this molten rock would

have coalesced into our moon relatively quickly, while the rest of the material fell back to Earth to help it re-form. The cosmic collision theory is also backed up by comparisons between the isotopes found on Earth and those on the moon. They are identical, which suggests a common source.

The moon has a solid, iron-rich inner core, a fluid outer core of liquid iron that gives it a weak magnetic field, a thick mantle and a thin crust

ABOVE
The Apollo landing sites marked on the surface of the moon.

LEFT A photo of Earth taken by the crew of Apollo 17.

to be over 300,000 impact craters more than half a mile (1 kilometre) across on its nearside alone. Most of these were thought to be of volcanic rather than impact origin but as new ones were appearing all the time it was eventually realised they must be formed during cosmic collisions. The dark and relatively featureless patches on its nearside are vast lava plains that do hint at a geologically active past, however, although there are hardly any on its far side. No water can survive on its surface because there is no evidence of a substantial atmosphere, but there may be pockets of ice trapped underground.

Americans Neil Armstrong and Buzz Aldrin became the first people to walk on the moon's surface when Apollo 11 touched down on 20 July 1969. Since Apollo 17 visited in 1972, no one has been back. If we are to continue exploring our solar system, however, it is likely that the moon will be used as a launching point: if water can be mined from below its surface, it will provide the two main ingredients of rocket fuel – hydrogen and oxygen – and its gravity is only about a sixth of the earth's so launches will be much less demanding.

of silica, alumina, lime and iron oxide. Its Aitken Basin crater is 1,500 miles (2,240 kilometres) across, which is the largest impact site known in the entire solar system. In fact there are thought

Mars

Mars is the fourth rocky planet from the sun. The high quantity of reddish brown iron oxide on its surface gives it a familiar colour (although it isn't really red enough to be called the Red Planet). The surface of Mars shows evidence of impact craters, liquid water and a thin atmosphere. Its surface was probably the site of one of the largest impacts ever in our solar system. The northern

hemisphere is smooth and sits at a lower elevation than the rough southern hemisphere. In the 1980s astronomer Stephen Squires and geologist Don Wilhelms suggested that this dichotomy could be explained by an impact with an object nearly the size of our moon. It happened around four billion years ago during the solar system's infancy.

Mars is about half the diameter of the earth and its surface area is comparable with that of our continents. It seems likely that Mars once had tectonic activity, a strong magnetic field and a substantial atmosphere but activity in the planet's iron core gradually slowed and the solar wind stripped away its atmosphere. Liquid water can't now exist due to its low surface pressure so it's frozen underground and at the poles. There is enough water to cover the entire planet to a depth of at least 33 feet (10 metres), however. At roughly 140 million miles (230 million kilometres) from the sun, Mars takes 687 Earth days to make one orbit and it rotates once about its axis every 24 hours and 40 minutes. If humans are to leave Earth in the distant future, Mars will be our first port of

call because plans to terraform the planet are already being considered.

The Asteroid Belt

Beyond Mars we come to the asteroid belt, a collection of rocks varying in size from fine dust particles to Ceres, which is more than 600 miles (966 kilometres) in diameter and large enough to be called a dwarf planet. The belt is usually represented on maps of our solar system as a dense cluster of rocks but this is far from the truth. Space is absolutely enormous and these rocks can actually be millions of miles apart. Indeed, we have sent several spacecraft

ABOVE
A close-up of a sample of moon rock brought back from the Apollo 11 mission.

LEFT
Neil Armstrong, Michael Collins and Edwin 'Buzz' Aldrin were the crew of Apollo 11. Collins remained in the command module and did not walk on the moon.

Deep Valleys
of the martian
surface. It is still
debated whether
the valleys
originate from
groundwater
springs or liquid
or magma flows
on the surface.

through the belt with no problems at all. It is thought that the rocks are the remains of a planet that never quite made it. It will now probably never form due to the gravitational tug from both Mars and the next planet out, the massive gas giant Jupiter.

Some of these asteroids represent a danger to Earth as they occasionally cross our orbit. One, Apophis, caused concern when initial calculations predicted it would hit the earth in 2029 or 2036. These predictions have since been revised but, although the chances of it hitting are extremely remote, it is large enough to cause widespread destruction.

Weighing up to 75 million tonnes, with a diameter of over 300 metres (1,000 feet) and travelling at more than 20,000 mph (32,000 km/h), an impact would release around 500 megatons of energy. By way of comparison, that's more than double the power of the Krakatoa eruption in 1883, 10 times the power of the largest nuclear bomb ever detonated, and at least 50 times the size of the impact that created Meteor Crater in Arizona.

Smaller asteroid impacts occur

BELOW An artist's impression of a probe approaching Vesta (L) and Ceres (R).

throughout the solar system all the time. If an object crashes into Mars, for example, it can blast fragments of the Martian surface back into space. These chunks of rock occasionally find their way to Earth as meteorites. This is yet another possible explanation for how life on Earth began – born

LEFT The scar on the Martian surface is a giant canyon system known as the Valles Marineris.

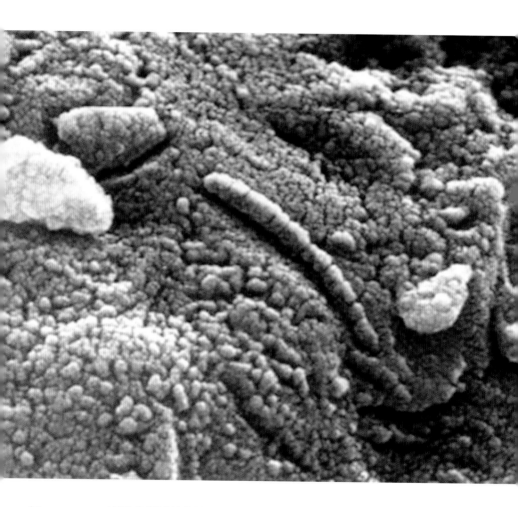

from an asteroid strike on Mars and then transported to seed the earth via meteorite. Most of these burn up in the atmosphere, and two-thirds that make it through are swallowed by the ocean, but some can be found (mainly in the deserts of Chile and Antarctica where spotting them is easier).

One of these, known as ALH 84001, was believed to have been blasted off the Martian surface by an asteroid impact millions of years ago before wandering through space and finally falling to Earth during the last ice age 13,000 years ago. It was found in Antarctica in 1984 by an American team of meteorite hunters. In 1996, the small piece of rock made headlines around the world when the science team examining it announced that they had found what could be the fossilised remains of Martian bacteria. They'd seen carbon structures under high-powered microscopes that were similar to primitive life forms on Earth. Then President Bill Clinton backed their findings which triggered both excitement and controversy. Some believed that the evidence for life was overwhelming, others that the sample could have become contaminated

during the thousands of years it had been on Earth, or that the structures weren't really fossilised bacteria at all. The fuss over the find has long since died down and the search for extraterrestrial life continues.

Jupiter

Jupiter is the fifth planet from the sun. This gas giant is the largest of the planets and could easily fit all of the others inside. As with all the major planets, it was known about from ancient times. It is composed mainly of hydrogen and helium, prompting many cosmologists to suggest that it could have been a star that didn't quite make it (most star systems are binary so the fact that we only have one sun is a little unusual). As a result, its atmosphere is extremely deep (3,000 miles or 5,000 kilometres), with a small rocky core surrounded by a layer of dense metallic hydrogen under extreme pressure at its centre. It used to be even hotter and larger, however, further evidence that it almost grew large enough to become a star before it contracted and cooled.

Jupiter's turbulent clouds of ammonia are whipped into intense

ABOVE The Shoemaker-Levy 9 comet leaves its mark on the surface of Jupiter. Some of the impact sites are larger than Earth.

storms, one of which, the Great Red Spot, is three times the size of the earth and has been raging for hundreds of years. At more than 500 million miles (800 million kilometres) from the sun, it takes Jupiter 12 years to make one orbit. Its day is extremely short, however, as it makes one rotation about its axis in just 10 hours (this means its equatorial rotational velocity is around 30,000 mph or 45,000 km/h, 30 times faster than that of the earth). The planet also has a faint ring system and at least 60 moons, four of which – Io, Europa, Ganymede and Callisto – were discovered by Galileo and could harbour primitive life. It is, in effect, a system unto itself.

In 1993, geologist Gene Shoemaker, his wife Carolyn and amateur astronomer David Levy found that a comet was on course to strike the gas giant. The orbits of comets are notoriously difficult to predict – some take over a million years to reappear – but Shoemaker-Levy 9 was found to have passed so close to Jupiter the previous year that its orbit had shifted. The planet's gravity had ripped it into 21 pieces, which had then spread out

like a string of pearls. Their calculations revealed that these fragments would strike the planet in 1994.

Reaction from the scientific community was mixed. The fragments were small and the planet enormous, so most observers reckoned Jupiter would swallow them without so much as a burp. Shoemaker believed the comet's speed would cause massive impacts

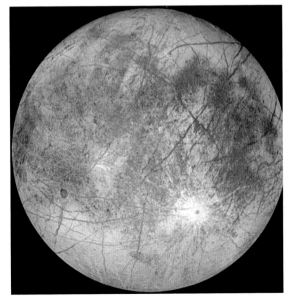

RIGHT There are storms and hurricanes on Jupiter the biggest of them is known as the Great Red Spot.

BELOW Jupiter has three thin rings called the Halo Ring, Main Ring, and the Gossamer Ring

hundreds of miles across that could be seen via telescope from Earth, but few of his contemporaries sided with him and most laughed at his theory, with some even labelling it The Big Fizzle.

It was Shoemaker who had the last laugh, however. The impacts were simply huge, with some of the fireballs tearing scars in the Jovian cloud tops the size of the earth. Fragment G, a two-mile-wide (three-kilometre) chunk of ice and rock, struck with the energy of six quadrillion tonnes of high explosive (six hundred times the power of the world's entire nuclear and conventional arsenal combined). If something this size travelling at that speed struck the earth, it would almost certainly extinguish all life. Shoemaker would doubtless have gone on to become one of the greatest astrogeologists but he was killed in a car crash while studying impact craters in Australia in 1997.

Saturn

Saturn is the second of the gas giants and the sixth planet from the sun. Its composition is similar to that of its neighbour in that it probably has a rocky core covered in a layer

of hot metallic hydrogen, layers of liquid hydrogen and helium, and then a gaseous layer on top. It radiates more heat into space than it receives from the sun through gravitational compression as well as friction between heavy helium droplets deep within its atmosphere. The planet takes nearly 30 years to orbit the sun, but, like Jupiter, it also revolves about its own axis in a short period, just 10½ hours.

Saturn has at least 60 moons but the largest, Titan, accounts for almost all the mass in orbit around the planet. The satellite has a nitrogen-rich atmosphere, plenty of water ice and hydrocarbon lakes on a rocky surface that is quite similar to Earth. Titan is seen as a potential haven for microbial life as many of the same processes – wind, rain, sand dunes and rivers – that we are familiar with also exist there. It is Saturn's ring system that is its most notable feature, however.

The rings extend 71,000 miles (114,000 kilometres) from an initial altitude of 4,000 miles (6,400 kilometres) and they consist mostly of water ice with a little carbon and other impurities. They are made

ABOVE
A false colour image revealing Titan's thick atmosphere.

from tiny particles to chunks about 30 feet (10 metres) across but the rings themselves are only about 70 feet (22 metres) thick. The apparent gaps between them are misleading as some have been caused by moons and others don't exist at all – they are simply bands where the material

is not as reflective or dense. How they formed is not known but they could be the remnants of a moon that broke up under Saturn's gravitational attraction, or one that was hit and broke apart after a cosmic collision, or that the material was simply left over after Saturn's original formation. Some larger chunks appear to form when the ice clumps together but they are usually broken up by impacts with neighbouring clusters relatively quickly.

Uranus

The next planet out from the sun is Uranus. It is just visible with the naked eye but William Herschel used a telescope to confirm its existence in 1781, the first time the solar system had been extended in modern history. He wanted to call it George's Planet after the king but Uranus was eventually chosen as the Latinised name of the Greek god of the sky. Although its composition is similar to that of the gas giants already mentioned, it contains a lot more water and ammonia ices, hydrocarbons and a larger core of ice and rock. It also has a faint ring system (probably the result of another cosmic collision between a couple of moon-like objects), magnetic field and several satellites. Of the 27 known moons, the largest, Titania, only has a radius of around 500 miles (800 kilometres), which is less than half that of our own moon.

The planet orbits the sun once every 84 years because it lies about two billion miles (three billion kilometres) from the centre of the solar system, but it also rotates reasonably quickly about its own axis, completing one revolution in 17 hours. This axis is tilted at an angle of nearly 100°, however, so each pole gets 42 years of sunlight followed by 42 years of darkness. This unusual attitude is likely to have been caused by a collision with a planet the size of the earth during the formation of the solar system.

Neptune

The eighth planet from the sun is Neptune. Because Uranus's orbit couldn't be explained unless there was another planet beyond it that was exerting some gravitational influence on it, Neptune became the first planet to be predicted rather than observed directly. It was finally discovered in

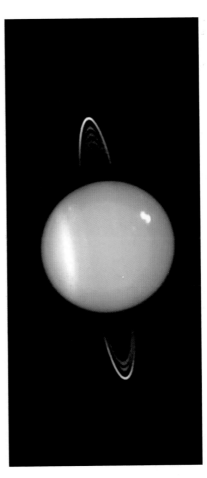

LEFT
A cosmic impact has knocked Uranus on its side, but its faint ring system is clearly visible.

1846 by Johann Galle within a degree of its predicted orbit (Galileo had observed it in the early 17th century but mistook it as a fixed star, and Urbain Le Verrier and John Couch Adams also came close to finding it but didn't have the right equipment). It has at least 12 moons, only one of which, Triton, was seen immediately. The rest were only discovered in the 20th century. Triton has a retrograde motion when compared with that of its parent planet, which indicates it was captured by Neptune's gravity rather than gradually forming into a moon from orbital debris. This means it probably came from the Kuiper Belt (see below).

Neptune and Uranus are similar in size (17 times the mass of the earth as opposed to 15), density ($1.6g/cm^3$ to $1.3g/cm^3$) and composition (mostly hydrogen and helium), and they are both icy gas giants with a relatively small rocky core. Where Uranus's weather is rather bland, however, Neptune's is much livelier. In 1989 the Voyager 2 spacecraft recorded surface wind speeds of 1,300 mph (2,100 km/h), and, at more than three billion miles (4.5 billion kilometres) from

the sun, it rarely gets above -220°C (-364°F) at the surface. There is warmth at the planet's core, however. It takes around 165 years to make one orbit of the sun. It also boasts a powerful magnetic field and remnants of a carbon and ice ring system.

The Kuiper Belt

Although it has recently been downgraded to a minor or dwarf planet, Pluto is probably the largest Kuiper Belt object (it is still only about one-sixth the mass of our moon). This belt of small icy worlds stretches from Neptune to about six billion miles (nine billion kilometres) from the sun and is littered with methane, water and ammonia-rich plutoids like Haumea, Makemake, Eris (which is about the same size as Pluto, although it is three times further from the sun), Sedna and Quaoar. Every so often, Neptune's gravity tugs on these worlds and they become visible via their orbital fluctuations.

For most people, this is where our solar system ends, but the reality is somewhat different. And it has a significant bearing on whether we'll

be able to travel beyond our system in the foreseeable future. Light from the sun takes around seven hours to reach Pluto, but the Voyager spacecraft (and any spacecraft we can build with current technology) could only travel at a fraction of that speed. The Voyagers took more than 12 years to reach the Kuiper Belt. But the real nail in the coffin is the fact that the Kuiper Belt is only 1/2500th of the way to the edge of our solar system, so it would take a minimum of 30,000 years to reach it. I'm afraid travel on this timescale simply isn't possible, and nor is it ever likely to be with our resources and technical know-how.

The Oort Cloud

Way beyond the Kuiper Belt it is believed that there is a cluster of celestial bodies, mainly asteroids and comets, in a band known as the Oort Cloud (it was first suggested by Estonian astronomer Ernst Öpik before his theory was revised by Dutchman Jan Oort, whose name stuck). This is where the sun's gravitational influence finally becomes so small that it is almost zero. Although no one has seen the cloud or its comets

(not even the Hubble Space Telescope can pick out such small objects at these great distances), astronomers believe Halley's Comet and the other long-period comets that occasionally enter the inner solar system probably originate in the cloud. It is thought that the cloud is the remains of the nebula that spawned the solar system in the first place but that the gravitational fields of the gassy outer giants prevented further planets from forming. Beyond the Oort Cloud, space would seem very peaceful and uncluttered (even though there should be trillions of comets and small asteroids in the cloud itself, they would be millions of miles apart). The sun wouldn't even be the brightest star in the sky. It's strange to think that we can overcome Earth's gravity quite

ABOVE The Hale-Bopp Comet probably originated in the Oort Cloud.

LEFT Dutch astronomer Gerard Kuiper gave his name to the belt of trans-Neptunian objects.

OUR SOLAR SYSTEM

easily when we pick up an object from the floor, but this same force keeps massive planets, asteroids and comets in orbit around the sun at distances almost beyond our imagination. And it's to gravity that we turn next, because the battle lines have been drawn.

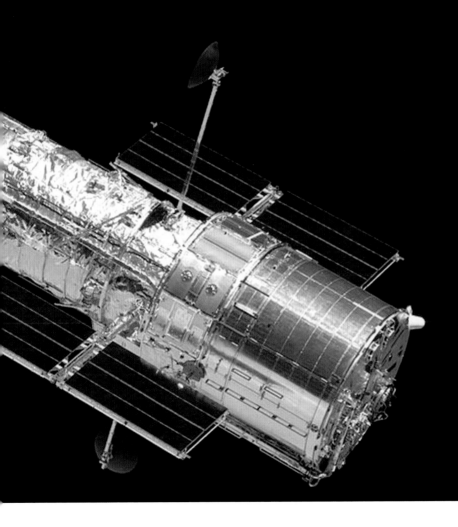

Matter & Dark Matter vs Antimatter & Dark Energy

It is commonly believed that when matter and its opposite, antimatter, were created during the Big Bang, an infinitesimal ripple in the fabric of space–time meant there was slightly more matter. When particles of the two collided during the evolution of the early universe, they annihilated one another in a ferocious burst of energy but, because of the slight initial imbalance, this violent episode left us with all the matter we see around us today. Indeed, everything in our universe that can be observed directly is made from the most basic building blocks of matter: atoms, which in turn are made up of a number of smaller particles like protons, electrons, muons, neutrinos and quarks.

None of these basic particles has yet been found to give an atom mass, however, which is why scientists are hunting for the elusive Higgs boson in particle accelerators (because they believe it will give everything mass). Once mass has been assigned, the problems of gravity can then be addressed. Until then, we are stuck in limbo without really knowing why gravity exists or how it works.

This gravitational problem can be illustrated on both small and large scales. Inside an atom, the electrons that fuzz around in a haze should spiral into the dense nucleus under the influence of gravity, but they don't. On a larger scale, the enormous mass of the galaxies in our universe should draw them towards each other, but, aside from local clusters that occasionally collide, all of the galaxies in the visible universe are accelerating away from one another. No one has yet been able to say why, but something must be driving that expansion.

And because gravity is so misunderstood, we have devised ways of making our equations fit with what

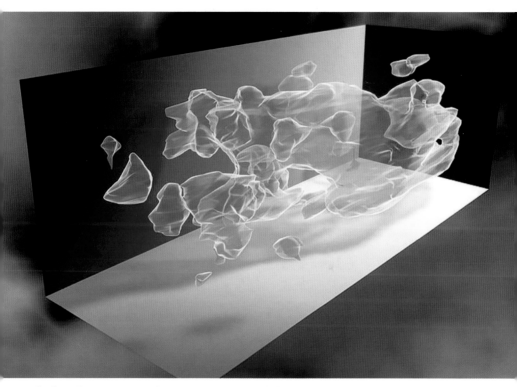

we think we know. Scientists have decided that most of the universe's mass must be missing and that this explains the motion of solar systems within galaxies. They've even given it a name: dark matter. And apparently it's everywhere: inside every cell in our body, in our homes, in our oceans and in the vast emptiness of space.

Swiss astronomer Fritz Zwicky

had been hunting for supernovae (as they explode with roughly the same intensity, these events can be termed standard candles and are useful for measuring distances, and therefore the rate of expansion, across the cosmos) when he turned his attention to the Coma galaxy cluster in the early 1930s. He calculated the mass of the cluster and concluded that it should be much greater than could be accounted for by the stars it contained. As this matter appeared to be completely non-reflective, he called it *dunkle materie* or dark matter.

The main problem with this dark matter is that we can't see it. If we can't observe it, it's extremely difficult to prove it exists at all. American astronomer Vera Rubin stumbled onto the same issue in the 1960s when she was investigating galaxy rotation rates. By measuring the distances between stars, their relative masses and their speeds, she uncovered a big discrepancy between the predicted motion of a galaxy and the actual motion that could be observed. Something had to be responsible for this difference.

Newton's laws of motion stated that the closer an object was to the object it was orbiting, the faster it had to move. The further away it was, the slower it could travel through space. This can be observed today with satellites orbiting the earth and planets orbiting the sun. Rubin naturally assumed that the same would hold for stars orbiting the galactic centre.

It took her two years to measure the velocity of 90 stars in the neighbouring Andromeda Galaxy, but her results were unexpected: all of the stars were moving at 150 miles (250 kilometres) per second. When she looked at other galaxies she got the same result: all of their stars were also moving at the same high speed as those closest to the centre. This should have made it impossible for galaxies to form because the stars on the outer arms were travelling so fast that they should simply have overcome the distant mass at the galactic centre and flown off into deep space.

Her results could only be explained if each galaxy had much more mass than could be observed, which seemed unlikely. But they persevered anyway and, the more her team looked, the more they realised that, according to

maths and conventional physics, at least 90 percent of the galactic mass was invisible, possibly as much as 95 percent.

This came as quite a shock to the scientific community and many doubted her initial findings. Several teams set out to disprove her theory, but when her results were repeatedly replicated, that same community was forced to accept her findings. More teams then tried to find out what this extra mass was made of but, because it couldn't be seen and didn't affect, absorb or emit light, they dubbed it dark matter.

As supercomputers grew more powerful, it became possible to model the early universe in cyberspace. By inputting reasonable variables (approximate number and mass of stars, for example), scientists came up with several ways they believed the universe might have developed from early dust cloud to solar systems and then galaxies, but there was never enough mass for galaxies to form in their magnificent spirals, and their models repeatedly failed to replicate the results we can see with the Hubble Space Telescope. Something was clearly missing from their models, so they gradually added invisible matter that had measurable mass.

Nothing happened at first so they gradually added more mass to their equations. When there was five times as much dark matter as observable matter, they noticed that areas of gas and dust finally began to collect in little clumps (this probably happened about a billion years after the birth of the universe). As the computer ran through its 13.7 billion-year cycle, the clumps of matter eventually collected into larger structures and finally produced the familiar galactic spiral. Now all they had to do was prove this is actually what happened.

It was soon discovered that dark matter acts like a lens and distorts the light from distant galaxies, so it can be observed by default as it passes through nearer galaxies. The amount the light arcs shows us that even the galaxies closest to Earth are shrouded in a cloak of dark matter. The HST can actually be used to plot this arcing to give us a map of the dark matter in our universe. The results are surprising: there is far more dark matter than the matter we can see. It makes up around a quarter of everything that's out there, and galaxies tend to cluster where it is thickest (so although it doesn't react with light, it does feel the force of gravity).

Cosmologist Carlos Frenk then mapped the entire universe and discovered that the galactic clusters were linked with filaments (some called it scaffolding) of dark matter that permeated the entire cosmos, rather like the web of neurons in the human brain. The implications were staggering: dark matter actually enabled galaxies, stars and planets to form, without which there would be no 'us', no life at all in fact.

In 2004, two clusters of galaxies four billion light years away were found to be colliding at 3,000 miles per second. One galaxy was so distorted by the gravity of the others that it took on the shape of a bullet, so cosmologists gave the event a name: the bullet cluster collision. During the collision, the visible matter within the galaxies interacted and distorted but the dark matter didn't react at all and passed through the collision completely unscathed. This provided scientists with yet another conundrum because although they

LEFT
Astronomer Edwin Hubble's red shift observations told us the universe was expanding.

MATTER & DARK MATTER VS ANTIMATTER & DARK ENERGY

knew dark matter could be affected by gravity, it clearly couldn't be affected by ordinary matter or even itself.

The race was now on to find and 'trap' a particle of dark matter so that it could be studied. Current scientific theory suggests that the particles that make up ordinary matter (protons, electrons, neutrinos and the like) may have dark super-symmetric mirror image particles that effectively exist in a different dimension and only interact with observable matter via gravity (dark matter normally passes straight through matter so they are only linked by gravity). Particle physicists tend to believe that dark matter is made up of weakly interacting large particles (WIMPs), while astrophysicists prefer it to be massive compact halo objects (MACHOs), which is another name for black holes. More recently, it has been suggested that, as no verified WIMP has ever been found (some have been claimed by Dan Bauer in his lab underneath Minnesota) and there simply aren't enough MACHOs to account for all the missing mass, perhaps we should call this invisible matter 'dark unknown non-reflective

non-detectable objects somewhere' (DUNNOS). Let no one say that scientists don't have a sense of humour.

It is believed that trillions of WIMPs pass through the earth every moment. Glimpsing one has not been easy, however. Even shielding our super-cooled germanium detectors beneath half a mile of rock has only yielded a couple of apparent WIMP strikes, but even they can't be absolutely confirmed.

Although matter and dark matter seem at odds with one another, they are both essential for the long-term survival of our universe. They both have their enemies, however. Visible matter is annihilated by antimatter (thankfully the former has the upper hand at the moment) and the dark matter that binds our galaxies together is threatened by a force that we know even less about.

In the 1920s the renowned astronomer Edwin Hubble surveyed the night sky and noticed that most of the galaxies in our universe were tinged red, which meant they were retreating from the Milky Way (just as sounds can change in pitch – think of the engine noise of a racing car – whether they're approaching us or hurtling off into the distance, so the light emitted by distant galaxies can change colour depending on whether they're coming towards us [blue] or moving away [red]). The inescapable truth was that if galaxies were all moving away from us, the universe must be expanding. If it was expanding, this process could, in theory, be rewound, giving rise to the notion that the universe must have come from a single point.

However, scientists then needed to work out how far away each galaxy was, which could only be reliably calculated by observing Type 1a supernova explosions (these always give off the same amount of light because they only occur when a white dwarf star in a binary system reaches the same critical mass). The further away the supernova was, the less light that reached us. It sounded simple but finding these supernovae proved almost impossible until a computer programme was developed to analyse deep field pictures from the Hubble Space Telescope. It was so sensitive that it could detect the explosions in galaxies at the edge of the known universe so

their positions could now be plotted.

Nobel Physics Prize Laureate Saul Perlmutter then inputted these results into a second programme. He expected to find that the expansion of the

MATTER & DARK MATTER VS ANTIMATTER & DARK ENERGY

universe would be gradually slowing down because of the gravitational attraction between galaxies. But he was in for a surprise. The galaxies in our universe were actually *accelerating* away from us. Not only that, they were also accelerating away from one another. This was totally at odds with the way gravity and dark matter behave, both of which were trying to bind the universe together. Something had to be driving this expansion, and it had to be so powerful that it could overcome the intergalactic gravitational attraction (even though gravity is seen as a weak force when compared with the strong and weak nuclear forces and electromagnetism, it still allows the earth to trap the moon in orbit). They eventually gave this mysterious force a name: dark energy.

In 2001, the Wilkinson Microwave Anisotropy Probe (W-MAP) was launched in the hope that it would measure fluctuations in the cosmic background radiation left over after the Big Bang. It actually ended up confirming the accepted age of the universe (13.7 billion years) as well as giving accurate data regarding its composition. W-MAP suggested that the ordinary matter with which we are so familiar only accounted for around five percent of the universe. About 23 percent was cold dark matter that neither emitted nor absorbed light, and approximately 72 percent was dark energy. This dark energy was what had so perplexed Einstein 70 years ago. He initially believed that a cosmological constant was driving Hubble's expansion but he was ridiculed at the time and later admitted that the hypothesis was the biggest mistake of his life. As so often happens with the great man, however, it seems now that he was right after all.

Its existence was finally proved beyond all reasonable doubt in 2011 when the WiggleZ survey of more than 200,000 galaxies confirmed that this dark energy-driven acceleration had been going on for at least half the age of the universe, around seven billon years. The energy-mass relationship encapsulated in Einstein's $E=mc^2$ suggests that every cubic centimetre of the universe stores a minute amount of mass in the form of this dark energy but that it is simply too small to be measured in our labs. As there are countless trillions of cubic centimetres in the universe, however, this adds up to considerably more mass than all the conventional and dark matter that we think exists.

The worry is that this mysterious force will one day overcome gravity and rip the universe apart. Scientists have now built a dark energy camera to plot the relative strength of the phenomenon. Has it always been driving the expansion of the universe, or did it have to overcome the powerful attraction of dark matter first? The answer depends on what dark (or 'phantom' as it's sometimes called today) energy actually is.

If it continues to gain in strength it will eventually begin to unravel galaxies. Then solar systems will be dismantled, and, finally, all ordinary matter, and that includes any life that still exists billions of years in the future, will be ripped apart atom by atom. For now, we'll have to pin our hopes on dark matter holding everything together.

Life

Perhaps the biggest question we face today is whether there is other life in the universe. As yet, the answer has eluded us, but, if physicist Frank Drake is to be believed, life positively flourishes in deep space and there are likely to be many advanced civilisations in our own galaxy. His theory is based on diminishing probabilities and can be summarised fairly easily.

The number of detectable civilisations in the galaxy at the moment should depend on several variables, such as: the rate of star formation within the Milky Way; the fraction of those stars which have solar systems (planets); the number of those planets that are in the zone that can support life; the number of planets where life actually develops; the chance of that life being intelligent and capable of transmitting information about itself into space; and the length of time for which that civilisation exists.

Some of the figures in the equation are reasonably easy to guess.

Astronomical observations, for example, suggest that around seven new stars are born in the Milky Way every year, and this rate has been measurably constant throughout its life. But there is a lot of guesswork over how many stars in our galaxy have planets that are in the habitable zone. We know from recent studies that at least 50 percent of sun-like stars have at least one planet. We know life could probably have existed on Mars at some point, and it may well exist in the oceans under the ice on Europa, but Jupiter's moon is outside the Goldilocks Zone (where the conditions to support life, such as having liquid water, are 'just right') so this clouds the issue.

Our best guess is that around 10 percent of stars have Earth-like planets orbiting them. And a recent study by astrobiologists Charles Lineweaver and Tamara Davis in Australia places a similar value on the chance of life evolving. Some scientists believe that once life has formed, it is inevitable that evolution will eventually lead to higher intelligence. Others counter this by saying that of all the millions of species that have existed on Earth,

only one has developed intelligence. Because of the wide variation in this parameter (practically zero to almost inevitable), the entire equation is likely to hinge on it. And if intelligent life did evolve, it may have happened millions of years ago and the civilisation may have gone extinct, so we need the number of intelligent life forms that are out there now.

Although we can hardly claim to be actively trying to communicate with other life forms, our radio transmissions and spacecraft are visible and audible so we could be detected by a distant civilisation. The lifetime of each detectable civilisation is another difficult parameter to predict. We know we have developed advanced technologies over a relatively short period of time, but we might go extinct tomorrow if the earth was hit by an asteroid. On the other hand, we might overcome our problems and survive as an intelligent species for millions of years.

Even with relatively conservative values for each stage, it's likely that there are several intelligent civilisations in the galaxy at the moment, but

LIFE

they would almost certainly be a minimum of hundreds of light years from Earth. Even if they had immensely powerful telescopes and could actually see the surface of our planet, they'd probably notice we were a primitive cave-dwelling society and want nothing to do with us. The nature of light, remember, means that we are looking back in time at all the objects in the cosmos.

The equation also raises religious questions. We know life exists here, but why should that be so? What gives us the right to exist when life might not have evolved somewhere else? This is probably also down to chance. Our universe is perfectly 'designed' for life to exist. It has the right balance of forces (gravity, electromagnetism and the strong and weak nuclear forces), the right mix of chemical elements, the right temperatures and pressures, and solid laws of science that allow life to form and evolve. Aren't we the lucky ones? However, many previous attempts to build universes may have failed. Big Bangs might have ended in Big Crunches, or the accepted laws of physics may not have come into being.

We only exist now because after all those failed attempts, the conditions in this one were just right. It's virtually a mathematical certainty that life would one day appear in a perfect place.

Because our universe is so unimaginably big, and there are countless stars like our sun with accompanying planets in the Goldilocks Zone, it seems almost inconceivable that life could not have evolved elsewhere. Indeed, the Milky Way is home to approximately 200 billion stars. How many planets they support is purely an educated guess, but there are still likely to be tens of millions that will have liquid water on their surface. And our galaxy is just one of more than 150 billion that make up the visible universe. These numbers are simply too big to comprehend. If life plays the lottery, it's got a good chance.

So, where should we be looking for life? If we can narrow the search down, we can then wonder what any aliens would look like. Their appearance would depend on a number of factors: the creatures on Earth, for example, are a certain size and shape because of the gravity we experience

and the oxygen concentration in the atmosphere. Animals that fly are usually small because air is not very dense and can't support their weight. Land animals can grow large because they can walk on a solid surface. And creatures that live in water can grow larger still because much of their mass is supported by the density of the fluid.

The medium in which the animal travels will also determine its appearance. Land animals need legs, for example. If the planet is within the habitable zone, it's likely to be well-lit by its parent star and eyes will be essential. Prey animals tend to have theirs on the sides of their heads so they can keep an eye out for predators. The latter tend to have forward-facing eyes so they can target their prey more easily.

Water, oxygen, carbon and sunlight are vital for almost all living things on our planet because most life-forms are carbon-based and need water to survive. As the laws of physics, at least at a visible level, appear to be universal, we, with no alternative to study, have to assume that the laws governing the development of life are also universal.

There is no doubt, however, that most alien species would find our world extremely hostile. We have taken millions of years to adapt to fluctuating oxygen levels (the gas was often toxic to our ancestors), for example. And whenever we venture away from our home planet, we need to take extreme precautions. The same would be true for any creature visiting us.

The earth formed from a nebula of cosmic dust and larger rocky debris more than 4.5 billion years ago, but no evidence for life appeared for another 700 million years. Amino acids are chains of carbon-based proteins that are essential for life. They can be created in the lab by mixing a few simple ingredients and are found naturally all over the planet but they are not themselves alive. So, this sterile clump of rock and minerals might have drifted silently through space for eternity had some of these chains not linked up and flickered to life as single-celled organisms. However life started, it then faced the problem of reproducing and passing its DNA on to its descendants. Life may have had several false starts before one primitive structure

LEFT
Owls have large forward-facing eyes and ear-holes.

divided in two and kick-started the process as we understand it today.

On Earth, all life seems to conform with a number of basic rules: it is conceived; its cells osmo-regulate (control the flow of fluid and food in and out) and grow; it breathes (not necessarily air); it feeds; it moves (responding and adapting to its environment); it reproduces (not necessary for an individual but it is for the survival of a species); and it dies (some simple organisms in New Mexico have apparently been revived after being inactive for 240 million years, and the cells of some plants and animals do not age in the conventional sense, but illness, starvation or climate change will eventually kill everything). As these constraints have evolved alongside the species on Earth, it seems likely that similar processes will apply across the cosmos for other life forms.

Another miracle of life as we know it is that for such a complex and poorly understood process, it doesn't need complex ingredients. Take some carbon, hydrogen, oxygen and nitrogen – simple elements that can be found all around us – then add a little calcium, sulphur, iron and a few other ingredients from the periodic table and you can make anything from a blue whale to an amoeba. All that is needed is the spark to breathe life into it. On Earth, this probably happened by chance when just the right sequence of molecules happened to collide. It's another curious fact that since life first took hold, not a single one of your ancestors – amoeba, slime, fish, reptile, burrowing rodent, primitive ape – died before passing on its genetic information. You are at the end of an unbroken bloodline stretching back nearly four billion years. If you think life isn't precious, think again.

While this may also be true out there in the cosmos, it's not essential. Alien life on some planets might be simple, such as slimes and single-celled organisms. On others it might have developed into more complex structures. Still more may have developed a reliance on methane or ammonia as variants of the carbon theme that allows us to exist. It's almost inevitable that if life has developed, so has the struggle for survival.

It may not seem like it to us with

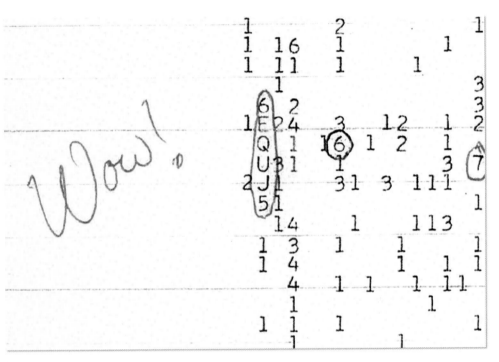

all of our modern conveniences, but all life on Earth is locked in a battle for survival. The two main priorities for us are to eat and procreate to ensure the continuation of our species. When Darwin first suggested this, people were outraged that the meaning of life could be so horribly simple, but his view has never been seriously challenged. It is highly likely, therefore, that life on other planets has the same priorities, so evolution will be a driving factor in what kind of creatures live out there.

We, as curious humans, really want

to know if life elsewhere has developed advanced technologies for travelling through space and time. We want to know if we've been visited before or if we will be again. One of the problems with understanding our universe is that it's a strange place, stranger than we can possibly imagine. It's easy for us to picture aliens like us on a planet rather like ours, but what if life took the form of microscopic clouds of dust that travelled on the solar winds, or if it had developed to the point where it was mechanised and could self-replicate, or if it came into and out of existence in the blink of an eye? Evolution is a powerful force of nature on Earth and we think we understand how it works (organisms tend to evolve as a reaction to the evolution of predators or in the face of changing conditions), but it may work differently out there in the cosmos. Life may have evolved to rely on silicon instead of carbon, for example.

There is another theory about how life might have made it to Earth, and it's called panspermia. Our planet has had a tempestuous past: it has been bombarded by meteorites, asteroids and comets for its entire life. And some of these bundles of rock, dust and ice contain the amino acids necessary for life. Indeed, it is now thought that much of the planet's water was delivered by comets from the Oort Cloud. If so, life could have been seeded by these alien visitors. While this sounds like an interesting theory, it does beg the question: if life didn't begin here, where did it begin? Panspermia merely moves responsibility for life's genesis somewhere else. Many scientists believe it could even have come from somewhere as close as Mars.

The red planet has intrigued us for centuries, but it is only recently that we are beginning to understand it. Mars has a great deal of frozen water at its poles, and it almost certainly still has water beneath its surface. NASA's Spirit Rover recently uncovered salt deposits beneath the rocks that only form on Earth in contact with liquid water so, although we haven't yet found life on Mars, it may be that some small organisms still exist underground. The vast drainage patterns that criss-cross its surface also hint at a past where liquids flowed over

LEFT
NASA's Spirit Rover.

the plains and through its canyons.

It is thought that liquid water still exists under the icy surface of Jupiter's moon Europa. And of all the places in our solar system to hunt for life, this may well be the place most likely to yield an exciting discovery. It's too far away for us to send a manned mission yet, but probes will arrive in our lifetimes.

Although the surface temperature falls as low as -220°C (-364°F), and the ice may be up to 15 miles (26 kilometres) thick, Jupiter's immense gravitational field stretches and compresses the moon's interior as it orbits the planet, generating heat through friction in its rocky core. The heat would melt the underside of the ice sheet and the water it produced would be protected from the vacuum of space by the remaining icy shell.

We believe that all life on Earth relies on the sun, as its heat and light allows plants and animals to grow. So how could life evolve under such extreme conditions on Europa? The answer can be found at the bottom of our oceans. Colonies of marine organisms have been found living in ecosystems around volcanic hydrothermal vents that don't

rely on our sun at all. The minerals and chemicals ejected by the vents provide the shrimp-like crustaceans and flora with all the sustenance they need for survival and the same could be true on Europa. It may well be that despite searching the heavens for the one-in-a-billion radio signal emanating from another civilisation, we could find life flourishing much closer to home.

Indeed, in the last half century, we have only heard one potential message from space, the infamous 'Wow!' signal that was picked up by researcher Jerry Ehman on the Big Ear radio telescope in Ohio in 1977. It was a steady source of radio waves that stood out because it was on a completely different wavelength from all the background radiation. Despite returning to the same area of the cosmos over the following years, the signal had disappeared. Making contact with aliens via radio signals is always going to be problematic. Even though they travel at the speed of light, it would still take more than eight years to get a reply from an advanced civilisation living on a planet orbiting the nearest star after the sun, Proxima Centauri.

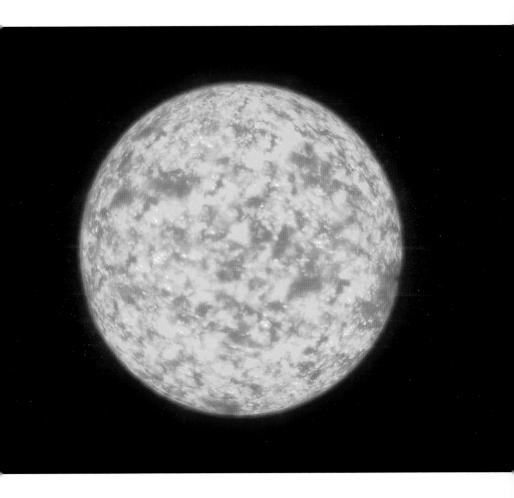

The international space station is the pinnacle of our technological advances. We have a long way to go as a species before we can explore the deeper universe.

We have been transmitting radio waves into space for a little over 80 years, so our first signals (like the 1936 summer Olympics) are now 80 light years from Earth. Alien civilisations might well be enjoying watching Jesse Owens win his historic four gold medals in Berlin. But Stephen Hawking believes it might not be such a good idea to announce that we are here. Advanced civilisations might have learned to control the processes by which they age, so they may in fact be immortal. Their technologies might be as extraordinary to us as the space shuttle is to a chimpanzee. And they might also be locked in a struggle for survival beyond their own solar system having exhausted their planet's natural resources. Aliens wandering the cosmos in search of resources to ensure their survival would almost certainly be hostile, and we wouldn't want them to find our planet with all its riches.

If there were civilisations within 50 light years of Earth, we might have heard them by now, but the number of stars within range is tiny when compared with the entire Milky Way. Over the next few thousand years we might get lucky because, as the Drake Equation suggests, it's all about numbers and probability.

The problem with proving the equation is simply one of time and space. The space between stars and their accompanying systems is vast, too vast to be crossed by our spaceships or even with technologies of the foreseeable future. Because the distances involved are so great, we simply don't have time to cover them. To do that, we'd need a spaceship capable of carrying and supporting a breeding population of humans that could travel at nearly the speed of light. Even at our current rate of progress (computing power and technological advancements develop exponentially), we won't be able to build such a craft with its advanced propulsion system for thousands of years. And it would be a financial burden that no country could shoulder.

To cover the distances involved in a reasonable timeframe means we'd have to find a way to bypass Einstein's laws on faster-than-light travel, which, as we've already seen, is not possible at the moment.

The Future

If we accept there was a big explosion at the start of it all, and we are reasonably confident of our position today, we can use maths and physics to deduce with great accuracy what happened in the intervening years, and we can also use the same tools to predict what will happen in our future.

We have now begun the search for Earth-like planets in other solar systems. If this sounds like a complex, time-consuming and expensive operation, you'd be right. Stars, even the distant ones in our galaxy, are extremely bright. And any planets that orbit them are consequently pretty dim. So how is it possible to find a planet tens of billions of miles away? And, having found one, how do we know what it's like?

The first part is relatively straightforward. Even small planets have a gravitational influence on their parent star. As they orbit around it, they pull on the star and cause it to wobble (much like a hammer thrower as he spins). Our best telescopes can detect these faint dances and can then predict with reasonable accuracy how big the planet is and how far from the star it orbits. A second method involves monitoring the relative brightness of each star. Planets occasionally pass in front of them (from our line of sight), so their light dims. Again, we have telescopes that can map these tiny fluctuations in the amount of light given off by the star. When it dims, a planet is passing in front of it like the recent transit of Venus in our own solar system.

We can now plot how often these transits take place, and, because we can then work out how fast the planet is moving, we can predict if it is in the Goldilocks Zone. The same is true for those planets that make their star wobble. Because the mass of the planet can be estimated reasonably accurately (the variation in the wobble can be used to determine planetary mass), and its distance from its star can also be plotted, we can now say with a high degree of probability whether any planets we find

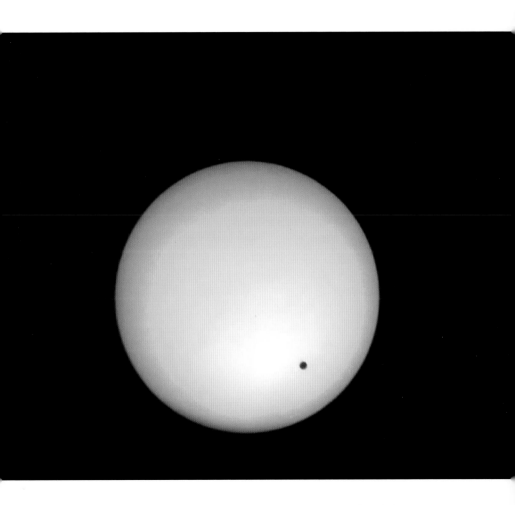

could support liquid water. Hundreds of these planets have now been found so, if we want to find life, this is where we should be looking. As we will not be able to travel to these distant worlds for the foreseeable future, we'll have to send them radio messages instead and hope that we get a reply sometime.

It seems that most of the planets out there, however, are gas giants like Jupiter and Saturn. If so, life may have evolved that utilises these conditions. Perhaps the biggest question is whether or not intelligent life has evolved. It's all very well to talk about single-celled organisms or primitive creatures, but we really want to know if there are civilisations out there with technologies more advanced than ours. If so, we'd like to meet them. As the Drake Equation is refined further, it's clear that any life in our galaxy is likely to be a long way from us and we certainly won't be hearing from them or visiting them soon. They would have to come to us, assuming they had the technology.

Of course many people believe that aliens have *already* visited us, and more believe that they still walk among us, but however romantic this sounds, it's extremely unlikely. Intelligent aliens with spaceships that can cross interstellar space at incredible speeds are unlikely to bother travelling all this way to make the odd crop circle or kidnap a lone individual. Almost all UFO sightings can be accounted for (strange atmospheric phenomena like earthquake lights, secret military aircraft, meteorites, misidentified everyday objects, ball lightning, hoaxes etc), although a few still confuse us today. The simple fact is we don't know everything about our own planet and it still throws up the odd surprise.

And the wider universe looks like it's got plenty of surprises in store for us too. In 2008, Alexander Kashlinsky and his team published a paper on the relatively unknown science of something called dark flow. A cluster of at least 700 galaxies was being drawn towards a distant point beyond the constellations of Centaurus and Vela. This contravened the expected motion predicted by Hubble's Law and the cosmic microwave background radiation which suggested that galaxy clusters should be randomly distributed throughout the visible universe.

Kashlinsky hypothesised that as the galaxies were travelling towards a mass beyond the particle horizon shortly after the Big Bang (the point at which light from the early universe left on its way to us), the gravitational source must be outside the visible universe. A number of suggestions have since been made, some saying that it might be another universe and others believing that it may be invisible matter in a different dimension.

Conventional science doesn't like to deal in multiverses (more than one universe) but string theory is gaining wider support and it can help explain the problem. Indeed, some believe that the theory can help unify quantum mechanics and General Relativity into a grand theory of everything, the Holy Grail for physics. It has always been thought that subatomic particles are both massless and dimensionless, but string theory and its latest incarnation, M-theory, endorsed by none other than Stephen Hawking, suggests that these particles are in fact one-dimensional strings that exist in 11-dimensional space made up of membranes. If you find this hard to grasp, you are not alone.

LEFT
Proponent of dark flow, Alexander Kashlinsky.

Remember that dark matter and dark energy are invisible to us so they could be said to be in a different dimension. The membranes described by string theory can be enormous and contain entire universes within themselves. Some scientists believe that when these membranes inadvertently collide, they cause Big Bangs. If they are indeed universes as part of a larger multi-verse, it might help explain some of the galactic motion within our visible universe, although science is undecided as to whether gravity can cross the boundaries between universes. No doubt these theories will be expanded and amended in due course.

Science-fiction authors describe many weird and wonderful technologies in their works, but how many of these futuristic gadgets are in development, and has their writing influenced what we already use today?

Antigravity devices have been in the pipeline for as long as the force has been written about. However, despite claims by Russian scientist Dr Yevgeny Podkletnov that he has developed a machine for altering gravity, nothing has worked yet. The problem seems

to revolve around the mechanisms by which gravity works. Essentially, gravity is a product of the warping of space-time by any object with mass. We all bend space and time but, as we have such little mass, we don't really notice it.

Planets, stars and galaxies, of course, are considerably more massive. Overcoming their gravity, which is the key to cheap spaceflight and travel between solar systems, must have been mastered by any UFOs visiting us. The problem is that we don't *fully* understand how gravity works. Current scientific thinking suggests that a minute particle in the centre of atoms, the as yet undiscovered graviton, is what mediates the force of gravity. If we find this particle after a collision in the Large Hadron Collider, we might eventually be able to manipulate it, and that could result in the production of antigravity devices.

The second particle we need to find is the elusive Higgs boson, which should assign mass to the atom itself. Again, should it eventually be found, our greater understanding of the structure of the atom might help us to manipulate gravity.

Time-travel might also be possible if we can manipulate gravity, because it will give us some control over the fabric of space-time. By effectively folding space back on itself, we could travel to distant parts of the cosmos in a fraction of the time it would take in a conventional spacecraft, faster even than the time it would take light to make the journey.

Even if space-time can't be manipulated, the faster a spaceship travels, the quicker it moves into the future. So, if UFOs have ever visited us, travelling billions of miles across space at incredible speeds, they would arrive back at their home planet thousands of years in the future. To do this would require propulsion systems that have not yet been invented on Earth. Perhaps one day the aliens will share their blueprints for antimatter reactors, hypersonic combustion ramjets, wormhole generators, magnetoplasma rockets, ion drives, teleportation devices and antigravity systems, or maybe they already have…

So what does our universe have in store for us? At the moment conditions on Earth are perfect for supporting

LEFT
An artist's rendering of a deadly gamma ray burst.

RIGHT
Gliese 581 d
could be a rocky
planet much
like Earth.

life. We live in the habitable zone and, unless we drastically alter our climate, life should continue to flourish for the foreseeable future. But there are forces at work in the cosmos over which we have no control. It is not within our power, for example, to deflect or destroy an inbound asteroid or comet like the one that wiped out the dinosaurs. And there are millions of cosmic bullets out there with our name on them. It only takes one collision between them, or for Jupiter to tug one slightly away from its current orbit, for one to be redirected towards the earth.

Contemporary science tells us that the impact on the Yucatan Peninsula 65 million years ago was so severe that the impact debris started fires across the globe. The soot blocked out the sun and affected the climate on our planet for many hundreds of years. Plants died, as did the animals that fed on them. In the end the food chain collapsed and 75 percent of all the species on Earth were wiped out. And this was all triggered by the impact of an asteroid just six miles across, a tiny object when compared with the size of the planet. It's a grim reminder that

our universe can still be a dangerous place. And there are more dangers closer to home: super-volcano eruptions, continental drift, climate change and disease also pose a serious threat.

In the long term, the gradual drift of the moon from its current orbit will create no end of problems for our descendants. It is receding from Earth at about two inches (five centimetres) per year so in another few hundred million years its effect on our tides will have all but evaporated. However, the moon also regulates the amount of earthly wobble that we experience. Remove it and there would be wild swings of the Earth's rotational axis and changes to its orbit around the sun, both of which would bring about catastrophic climate change that would probably make the planet uninhabitable.

Although it's tempting to believe that we are the end product of evolution, this would be a dangerous assumption. We are still evolving and, as other early human species like Neanderthal Man found out, the more intelligent species usually prevails. This is not always the case, however. Survival of the luckiest and not necessarily the

LEFT
Saul Perlmutter concluded that dark energy must be driving the expansion of the universe.

fittest has played a role in evolution. The dinosaurs were our planet's apex predators until conditions changed and they became extinct. It wouldn't even need an asteroid impact to put us in deep trouble – the mutation of a simple disease could do it.

The fossil record shows us that intelligent creatures usually last for about four million years, so we could be on borrowed time already. Simple life like bacteria, however, is virtually indestructible and it is they who will inherit the Earth (if they don't dominate it already). We could also be the architects of our own downfall. The threat of nuclear war may have subsided in recent years but we still have the power to destroy much of our planet. We may have the intelligence to build these weapons, but do we have the intelligence not to use them?

In the Milky Way a star dies roughly every 50 years. This doesn't sound very often, but over billions of years, it adds up to quite a few. And the supernova explosions they cause can affect solar systems for thousands of light years. They can also release an enormous amount of energy in the form of a

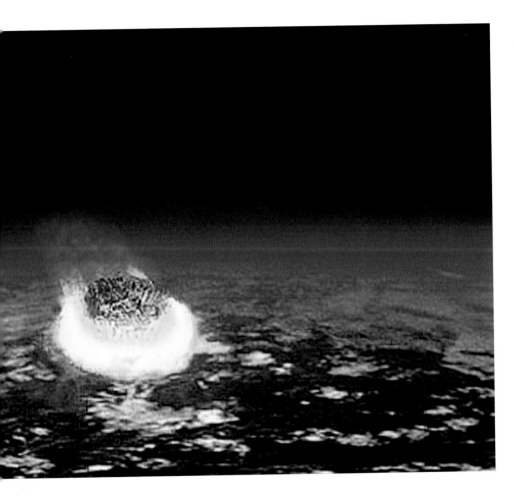

LITTLE BOOK OF THE **UNIVERSE**

gamma ray burst, an outpouring of deadly radiation from its poles that would incinerate anything within range. It's possible that one of the Earth's great extinctions around 450 million years ago was due to a gamma ray burst.

And our own sun will eventually expand so much that it will engulf the Earth before it explodes. Again, there's no need to worry just yet as our sun is only middle-aged and should be around for another five billion years or so. As it gradually expands into a red giant and grows hotter, it will force life to move further out into the solar system. It will one day swallow Mercury, Venus and Earth.

A solution to all these problems is already being devised, however. Humans first set foot on the surface of another world a little over 40 years ago, and this was the first step in colonising planets even further afield. We will one day go to Mars in what will be the second great step in an ongoing quest to explore the cosmos. As the sun continues to expand, life will have to adapt and hop between the planets until, eventually, it moves beyond its home system.

When our descendants move on,

LEFT
The Sun is very slowly expanding and getting brighter right now.

THE FUTURE

they will no doubt head for planets like Gliese 581d, a rocky super-Earth in the habitable zone, and one of five planets orbiting the star Gliese in the constellation Libra about 20 light years away. As usual, the main problem getting there will be the time it takes to travel 20 trillion miles (32 trillion kilometres). Even by hitching a ride on Voyager 1,

which, having been launched in 1977 has travelled more than 13 billion miles (20 billion kilometres) and is now the fastest and furthest manmade object from Earth, it would still take over 350,000 years to reach Gliese.

There is a way round this problem, however. Travellers of the future will be placed in suspended animation so they can make the journey without suffering the physical and mental degradation that occurs with age. Indeed, we will probably be able to modify our genes to halt the ageing process completely. Manipulating our genetic codes might also allow us to resist infection or radiation, breathe normally toxic gases, or design artificial life-forms with synthetic DNA to work for us.

So what does the future of our universe look like? There are three options favoured by scientists: the first is that the universe continues expanding at an increasing rate, powered by dark energy until it is a vast but ultimately cold and lifeless place. Without any gases or nebulae to form stars and planets, the universe would gradually grow dimmer as its stars blinked out. With its heat lost, even its black holes would

THE FUTURE

**RIGHT
& FAR RIGHT**
Big Freeze
is a possible
scenario in which
the Universe
will continue
to slowly cool
as it expands,
becoming
inhospitable
to life.

eventually dissipate and the universe would die in a phase known as the big chill or the big freeze. It won't happen for another 30 billion years or so, which is unlikely to affect you and me.

The second possibility is that gravity eventually overcomes dark energy and draws the galaxies and all other matter back to a single point in an exact reversal of what has happened so far. All of the mass and energy remaining would find itself in a singularity that may or may not explode into existence in another Big Bang. This may or may not have happened countless times in the past of course.

The third option is that the universe reaches a point where gravity and dark energy cancel each other out, leaving it in the steady-state so favoured by Fred Hoyle. If this happens, there is no reason why it shouldn't continue in that form forever.

Maybe one day we'll have all the answers about dark matter, dark energy, extraterrestrial life, dark flow, multiverses, string theory and time-travel, but, until we do, we'll just have to keep wondering about the amazing place that is our universe.

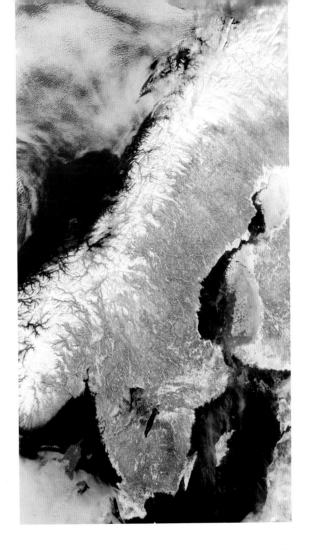

BELOW
Space Ship One,
a small step in
the development
of future space
travel.

BELOW
Space Ship One,
a small step in
the development
of future space
travel.

The pictures in this book were provided courtesy of the following:

GETTY IMAGES
101 Bayham Street, London NW1 0AG

WIKIMEDIA COMMONS
www.commons.wikimedia.org

Adam Evans - **Andromeda Galaxy**
J Kartik - **Arno Penzias**
Betsy Devine - **Alan Guth**
Steve Jurvetson - **Milky Way from the Black Rock Desert**
Campus Party Brasil - **Michio Kaku**
Johannes-Kepler-Observatory, Linz, Austria - **Hale-Bopp comet**
Holger Motzkau - **Saul Perlmutter**
M Bisanz - **Frank Drake's**
Debi Vort - **The Gliese**

Cover Design & Artwork: **DAVID WILDISH**

Published by: **DEMAND MEDIA LIMITED & G2 ENTERTAINMENT LIMITED**

Publishers: **JASON FENWICK & JULES GAMMOND**

Written by: **LIAM MCCANN**